STAR WARS REBELS

ANNUAL 2015

EGMONT

We bring stories to life

First published in Great Britain 2014
by Egmont UK Limited, The Yellow Building,
1 Nicholas Road, London W11 4AN.

Designed by Maddox Philpot. Written by Katrina Pallant.

© 2014 Lucasfilm Ltd & ™. All rights reserved.

ISBN 978 1 4052 7201 8
57508/1
Printed in Italy

CONTENTS

RESTORE THE REPUBLIC

EZRA

REBELS AGAINST THE EMPIRE

A streetwise orphan boy joins a band of rebels aboard their ship, the *Ghost*. The Empire is engaged in hunting down the remaining Jedi Knights and anyone else that does not fall in line. The *Ghost's* crew makes it their mission to disrupt the Empire's forces wherever they can through schemes and pranks. Their attempts at bringing freedom to the people oppressed by the Empire are dangerous, but this band of rebels is ready for adventure and willing to fight!

JOIN THE REBEL CAUSE BY FILLING IN YOUR STATS HERE.

Name: _____

Age: _____

Species: _____

_____

Homeworld: _____

_____

Special skills: _____

_____

Weapon of choice: _____

_____

ALL REBELS NEED BACKUP. FILL IN YOUR BEST FRIEND'S STATS TOO.

Name: _____

Age: _____

Species: _____

_____

Homeworld: _____

_____

Special skills: _____

_____

Weapon of choice: _____

_____

REBELLIOUS FRIENDS

```
L D L D B G K R M A B Z H R P
X B U Y C N R B K Q E P E C Y
Z C Z M T K P E O N Q P L B Y
E I X Y J F O H E R P G J F I
N G H O S T W X X O I T M B U
I L O A I Q P Z H U K F J J O
B X I A A L U C I X W S L D I
A Z J G O R F R N C L Z E E T
S O E S H C F D W P N A S F N
E L I G N T E G O C R B L G F
J U G O A A S L K Z O O I R N
E S L C N W N A E H A K N X N
Q B Y W A G F L B I G R G O Q
Y D R J K J F X B E T Q S N U
M A D M L A A B C Z R X H J F
I R M A F C Y I T I S Y O G T
S W H A R E H O J H R W T T S
```

Find the names of the rebels and their weapons of choice in this wordsearch.

Ezra   **Hera**
Kanan   **Chopper**
Zeb   **Sabine**

Ghost
Slingshot
Lightsaber
Explosive
Bo-rifle

7

THE YOUNG STREET RAT

NAME:
EZRA
BRIDGER

Ezra is an orphan who has grown up on the streets of Lothal. He is a small kid in a big galaxy and he's had to learn to look after himself. Ezra's survival instinct and remarkable reflexes come in handy when he joins the *Ghost's* crew and opposes the Empire!

TOP SECRET

Ezra has a major crush on Sabine – but she thinks he is too young. This doesn't stop him from trying to impress her though!

Age: 14

Species:
Human

Homeworld:
Lothal

Special skills:
Quick, clever, amazing thief and con artist, excellent reflexes, escape and infiltration skills

Signature equipment:
Wrist-mounted energy slingshot and stolen Imperial helmet collection

Likes:
Playing pranks on Chopper

Dislikes:
Zebs complaining

"THIS HELMET IS PROPERTY OF EZRA BRIDGER ... OR IT IS NOW, ANYWAY!"

Ezra and the *Ghost* crew are ready for action. Can you find five differences between these two pictures?

Colour in a lightsaber for each difference you find.

THE RELUCTANT JEDI

NAME:
KANAN
JARRUS

KANAN

REBEL FIGHTER
DEFEAT THE EMPIRE
RESTORE THE REPUBLIC

Kanan is the leader of the small band of rebels aboard the *Ghost*. He is a brave leader and commands the crew's missions with cunning and confidence. As a former Jedi apprentice, he is quick, alert and deadly. Kanan has turned his back on the Jedi ways but when he finds the force-sensitive Ezra he finds himself stepping back into the ideals of the Jedi Knights of old.

TOP SECRET

Kanan would never admit it, but he loves being the father figure to the *Ghost's* crew.

Age: 27

Species:
Human

Homeworld:
Coruscant

Special skills:
Jedi capabilities, excellent leader, cunning strategist

Signature equipment:
Lightsaber and gunslinger blaster

Likes:
Planning missions to take down the Empire

Dislikes:
Being told how to shoot

KANAN'S CODE

Kanan's band of rebels are his family, but what is the name of the group he previously belonged to and why did he leave them? Use the code to find out!

S	E	A	I	O	T

D	J	R	H	F

KANAN WAS IN THE...

_____

HE LEFT BECAUSE OF...

_____

THE PROTECTIVE PILOT

NAME:

HERA

SYNDULLA

HERA

Hera is the owner and pilot of the *Ghost*. She is the 'getaway driver' for the crew's heists and schemes. Hera is reliable, warm but excellent at thinking up schemes for the band of rebels. She is a true believer in the rebel cause and her ultimate goal is for liberation from the evil Empire.

TOP SECRET

Hera pretended to love Kanan so she could get him to join the rebel cause, but now she really does love him!

"DO I HAVE TO DO EVERYTHING MYSELF?"

Age: 24

Species:
Twi'lek

Homeworld:
Ryloth

Special skills:
Ace pilot, skilled shooter, making connections

Signature equipment:
Ghost

Likes:
Being in the cockpit

Dislikes:
When the *Ghost* is damaged

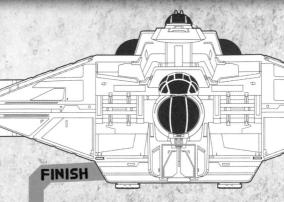

RACE TO THE COCKPIT

Hera needs to battle through the Empire forces to reach the cockpit of the *Ghost*. Help her through this maze but watch out for stormtroopers!

LIBERTY

FINISH

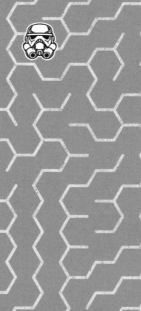

START

FREEDOM

THE MACHINE IN THE GHOST

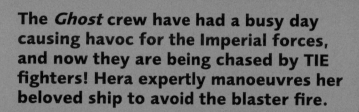

The *Ghost* crew have had a busy day causing havoc for the Imperial forces, and now they are being chased by TIE fighters! Hera expertly manoeuvres her beloved ship to avoid the blaster fire.

'Kanan, we have a small situation here,' Hera says through the intercom to the crew's leader. 'If you'd care to blast one of those TIEs out of the galaxy, I don't think anyone would object.'

Kanan quickly runs down the hallway to man the weapons in the Dorsal Turret. 'Working on it, Hera,' he replies as he takes his seat at the gun. 'Not like you gave me a lot of warning.'

'As I recall, raiding an Imperial convoy was your plan, love,' Hera quips.

Kanan blasts a TIE fighter out of the sky as the *Ghost's* shields deflect the attack from the remaining TIEs. Suddenly the shields fail and the rebel crew are hit by a sparking blaster shot.

'Shields down!' Hera shouts. 'Chopper, fix them!' Chopper, the *Ghost's* repair droid, arrives to help. He is cross, as usual, and does not appreciate Hera's impatience. Kanan shoots and misses. The *Ghost* is hit by another TIE fighter blast.

'Kanan, what part of "blast them" did you not understand?' Hera asks as the whole ship shakes. There is no response. 'Kanan? Kanan, do you read?' Hera bangs her hand on the dashboard. 'Internal comm is out. Chopper, go back to comm control and fix it!' Chopper beeps that he is busy, fixing the *Ghost's* shields.

'I know you are fixing the shields, but I need comm operational to coordinate our attack. Now go before I pull your battery!' Hera commands. 'And while you're back there, tell Kanan to please hit something!'

Chopper leaves the cockpit, grumbling all the way down the corridor.

Chopper beeps Hera's message to Kanan as he passes the turret.

'I'm a little busy, Chop. Wait, what are you doing here?' Kanan asks. 'Shouldn't you be fixing the shields?'

Chopper beeps.

'Did you say "fixing the comms"? I don't need to talk to Captain Hera right now,' Kanan shouts as he continues firing at the TIE fighters. 'Get back up there and fix the shields. And when you see Hera, tell her to fly better!'

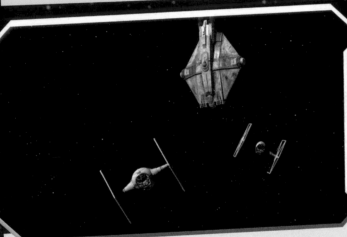

Chopper turns around and heads back to the cockpit. He is not happy that he is being bossed about. When he tells Hera what Kanan said, the annoyed pilot swings the ship around behind a TIE fighter and blasts it with the nose gun. It blows up, leaving just one TIE fighter in pursuit of the *Ghost*.

'Do I have to do everything myself?' she complains. 'There, I just reduced Kanan's targets by half. Tell our fearless leader he should be able to handle one lone TIE fighter on his own.'

Chopper is fed up of being the go-between for Hera and Kanan. But Hera does not want to hear his grumbles. He rolls away feeling sorry for himself.

Chopper rolls straight past the turret and Kanan and boards the *Phantom*. He plugs into the *Phantom's* cockpit and blasts a cannon shot at the remaining TIE fighter.

It explodes into atoms and the *Ghost* flies away, safe to fight another day.

'Alright, I admit it,' Hera says as Chopper re-enters the *Ghost's* cockpit. 'That was some fine shooting.' Chopper brims with pride – until he realises she is talking to Kanan.

'Thank you,' Kanan replies. 'You too.'

Chopper is furious.

'Just kidding, Chop!' laughs Kanan.

'We know you got that last one,' Hera adds. 'Good work. Now get that comm fixed! And don't forget the shields.'

Chopper is stunned for a minute, and then he rolls away grumbling. No rest for the wicked!

THE END.

THE LOUD LASAT

The people of Lasat were brutally defeated by the Empire but Zeb escaped. Whenever he fights the Imperial forces he does so for his people.

NAME: GARAZEB

'ZEB'

ORRELIOS

ZEB

Zeb loves to wind up his fellow crewmates, but he is very protective of his rebel family. He likes to bend the rules and has been known to walk away from a plan if a better opportunity appears in the course of a mission. This boisterous Lasat bickers constantly with young Ezra but the two bond over their shared love of adventure.

Age:
The human equivalent of 39

Species:
Lasat

Homeworld:
Lasan

Special skills:
Hand-to-hand combat, heightened strength and stamina

Signature equipment:
Bo-rifle – combination fighting staff and laser rifle, the traditional weapon of the Honour Guard of Lasat

Likes:
Punching stormtroopers

Dislikes:
His number one enemy, Agent Kallus

"RIGHT. SO I'M DEFINITELY GOING TO BE LATE."

ZEB'S BOOTCAMP

Zeb is getting ready to fight some stormtroopers and he wants you to help him, but you have to be ready. Play these games with your friends to sharpen your soldier skills.

KANAN SAYS

A good soldier has to be able to follow orders. One player is the leader, Kanan, and the rest of the players follow his instructions but only if he begins with the words 'Kanan says', e.g. 'Kanan says clap your hands'. If the leader does not say 'Kanan says', e.g. 'jump up and down', and a player follows the instruction, that player is out. The last player in is the ultimate soldier!

REBEL IN DISGUISE

Set up hats, scarves, sunglasses and other clothing you have to hand in two piles at one end of your garden then split your friends into two teams to line up at the opposite end. Team members then take it in turns to run up and disguise themselves and then run back to their team. The first team fully disguised wins!

REBEL STATUES

If the Imperial forces turn up you need to hide and be really still so you don't get caught! Practise by playing musical statues with your friends.

THE GRAFFITI GIRL

NAME:

SABINE
WREN

Sabine is full of energy and mischief. She specialises in creating explosives that leave a signature mark, the calling card of their rebel group. Sabine is a good soldier but she bristles when given strict orders. She is an adrenaline junkie and wants to cause as much disruption to the Empire as she can using her art and her gadgets.

TOP SECRET

While she sees herself a free spirit, Sabine cherishes the family bonds she has built up with the rebels.

"FORGET THE EXPLOSION ... LOOK AT THE COLOUR."

Age: 16

Species:
Human

Homeworld:
Mandalore

Special skills:
Explosives expert, street artist

Signature equipment:
Art supplies, handmade explosives, Mandalorian helmet

Likes:
Customising her possessions, tagging Imperial ships

Dislikes:
Authority

TAGGING TROUBLE

Sabine is tagging an Imperial ship. Help her perform this rebellious task and draw, colour and embellish some rebel propaganda graffiti!

THE ECCENTRIC DROID

Chopper is a cranky droid who has been rebuilt and patched together from other droid parts. The rebels put up with his ill-tempered nature because he is very skilled at fixing the *Ghost* and keeping it operational. The crew mostly ignores his grumpy attitude but Ezra loves to engage in a prank war with this little robot.

CHOPPER

NAME: C1-10P
A.K.A
CHOPPER

"BEEP BEEP BOOP."

Age:
Very old

Species:
Astromech Droid

Homeworld:
Unknown, acquired used

Special skills:
Starship repair, astrogation

Signature equipment:
Booster rocket, computer probe

Likes:
Playing pranks on Ezra

Dislikes:
Almost everything

DROID in DISGUISE

Chopper is a cranky but lovable droid. Can you spot the real Chopper?

HINT

He is different from all the others.

REBELS RULE

RACE OF THE REBELS

Time for a race! You and your friends are fighting it out to be the rebel leader. Play this game to see who gets to the *Ghost* first.

START

BEING A REBEL MEANS BEING A TEAM PLAYER. SWAP YOUR COUNTER WITH THE PLAYER TO YOUR LEFT.

YOU HAVE PULLED OFF A SUCCESSFUL MISSION. MOVE FORWARD TWO SPACES.

THERE'S ONE. SET FOR STUN!

THE STORMTROOPERS HAVE CAUGHT YOU. MISS A TURN.

REBELS STICK TOGETHER. MOVE THE PLAYER ON YOUR RIGHT'S COUNTER TO YOUR SPACE.

YOUR BLASTER IS JAMMED. MOVE BACK ONE SPACE.

FINISH

HER SMILE

On the dark streets of Lothal the stormtroopers are on patrol.

'Move along!' The commander shoves an innocent bystander to the ground. 'This is a restricted area.' The commander watches the scared bystander scurry away, oblivious to Sabine Wren scaling a high wall right behind him.

'*Ghost* to Spectre-5,' says Hera, over the radio. 'We're in position and ready for your diversion. In fact, maybe more desperate than ready.' Sabine steadily climbs to the top of the wall and looks out over an Imperial airfield. 'That's just fine,' she replies. 'Because I'm going in now.'

Sabine ducks down as a spotlight scans over the wall. When it's gone, she drops down onto the tarmac and runs up to a TIE fighter. She peers round the wing to see a patrol of stormtroopers. She quickly hides.

'You hear that?' one of the stormtroopers says.
'I don't hear ... wait, yeah. What is that?' the second stormtrooper asks.
'This way.' The stormtroopers ready their weapons and head towards the sound.

As they approach some TIE fighters they see Sabine Wren painting a huge, fluorescent purple phoenix onto the wing of the Imperial ship.

What do you think you are doing?' one of the stormtroopers shouts. 'Just making some improvements,' Sabine says as she continues her art. The stormtroopers look at each other before aiming their guns at the rebel. 'W-well stand down! Or we shoot!'

'So shoot,' Sabine laughs before ducking beneath the cockpit and dodging the stormtroopers' blasts. 'You call that shooting? I think you boys need a little more time at the practice range.'

'This is TK-626. There's an intruder on site.' The stormtroopers call in for back-up. 'Over here, bucketheads!' Sabine shouts as the two stormtroopers lose sight of her once again. They attempt to shoot her but she is too quick. 'Just follow the sound of my voice,' she teases. Sabine weaves her way through the TIE fighters as the stormtroopers chase her, blasting their guns.

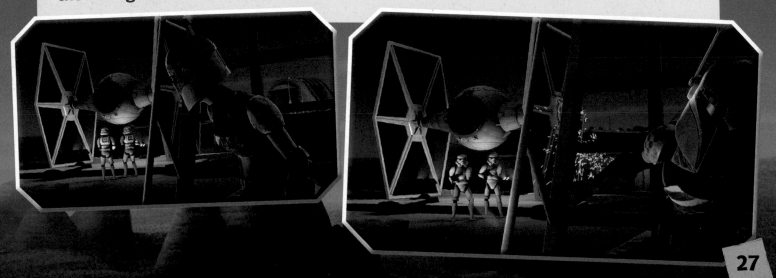

Four more stormtroopers arrive to help. 'What do we got?' the commander asks. 'One intruder in Mando gear, still at large,' the stormtroopers explain. 'Split up,' says the commander.

Sabine watches from atop a TIE fighter as the six stormtroopers go in different directions. Then she drops down to complete her phoenix. 'There. Perfect!' she declares.

The stormtroopers continue to search for Sabine. One trooper is moving between the ships when suddenly Sabine drops down behind him and sweeps his legs out from under him with a twirling kick. He rolls over to fire at the rebel, but she is already gone. 'Ha! Too slow.' Sabine laughs from her hiding place.

The stormtroopers are getting very angry now. They chase Sabine all over the airfield but every time they get close to catching her, she disappears. 'Intruder was headed your way!' shouts the commander. 'Sir, she was headed towards you,' responds one stormtrooper. 'Isn't this where we started?' says another.

They look to see Sabine's phoenix painting on the TIE fighter. There is a blinking LED light in the bird's eye. 'Uh oh.'

BOOM!

Sabine watches from a safe distance as the explosion lights up the sky. 'That was some diversion, Sabine,' Hera says over the radio. 'Did the job so well, we can see the explosion from here.'

Sabine removes her helmet to admire the purple and gold phoenix-shaped cloud rise above the airfield. 'Forget the explosion,' she says. 'Look at the colour!'

Sabine watches as the purple smoke clears, revealing the stormtroopers on the ground. They are all dazed and confused, and painted purple from head to toe! The artistic rebel puts her helmet back on and walks away, smiling.

THE END.

MY REBEL ADVENTURE

The *Ghost* has returned from a long mission causing havoc to the Imperial forces, but now she has broken down. Chopper is missing in action and they need a new droid to help with repairs. Draw one here.

Now that the *Ghost* is repaired it could use a paintjob. Colour in this rebel vessel and your own graffiti tags to it.

The rebels have landed on Lothal for another mission against the Empire. Write your own story about what happens next using the scene below.

Can you caption this picture? What do you think is happening?

_____

_____

_____

_____

The rebels have escaped after a particularly hilarious prank. Colour in the crew.

Ezra needs to hide quickly so he doesn't get caught by the Stormtroopers. Draw the newest rebel here in Imperial disguise.

SEEN A GHOST?

The *Ghost* is the rebels' home base. It is constantly on the move above Lothal to avoid detection, but occasionally docks in the wilderness or in rebel-friendly ports. The *Ghost* consists of four bedrooms for the crew, a common room, a galley, cargo bay, dorsal gun turret, the cockpit and a secondary auxiliary craft, the *Phantom*. The *Phantom* docks into the *Ghost's* tail section and is used for short-range fighting missions.

NAME: THE **GHOST**

HERA

Model:
VCX-100 light freighter

Owner:
Hera

Signature equipment:

Bubble gun port, electronic countermeasure systems – the *Ghost* has a variable transponder signature that allows it to assume false identities when picked up by distant scanners

FUN FACT:
Each crew member had their own room until Ezra came on-board, now Zeb must share his room with the newcomer, a fact Zeb never lets Ezra forget.

STARSHIP SAILING

The *Ghost* is lost in an asteroid field. Use the key to navigate through the maze and find the right exit so the *Ghost* can land.

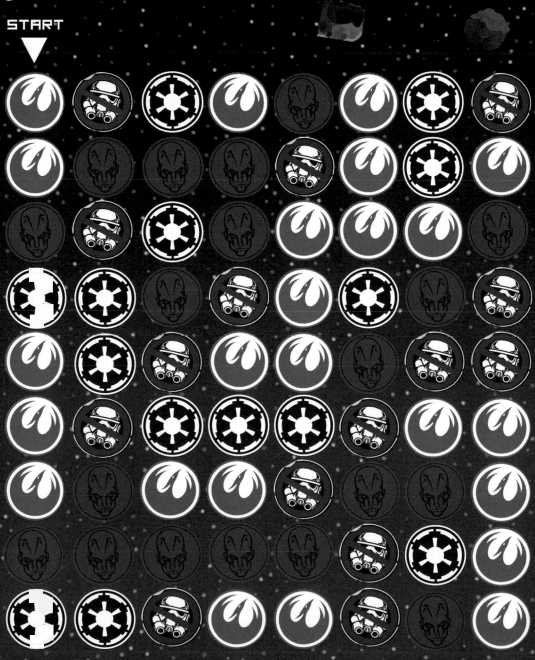

START

 =UP

 =DOWN

 =RIGHT

 =LEFT

A   B   C   D

WHICH REBEL ARE YOU?

1. WHAT IS YOUR FAVOURITE PASTIME?

a) Fighting

b) Flying

c) Fixing things

d) Painting

2. HOW WOULD YOUR FRIENDS DESCRIBE YOUR PERSONALITY?

a) Fearless and loyal

b) Protective and clever

c) Grumpy and sarcastic

d) Creative and daring

3. WHICH WEAPON WOULD YOU CHOOSE?

a) Bo-rifle

b) The *Ghost*

c) *Phantom*

d) Explosives

4. WHAT IS YOUR ULTIMATE DREAM?

a) To protect people

b) To own your own starship

c) To be appreciated by your friends

d) To create a masterpiece

5. IF YOU SEE A GROUP OF STORMTROOPERS WHAT DO YOU DO?

a) Attack

b) Call for back-up

c) Run away

d) Play a prank on them

ANSWERS:

Mostly As: You are like Zeb. You think before you act and often get yourself into trouble, but your heart is in the right place. You would never let anyone hurt your friends.

Mostly Bs: You are like Hera. You are the peacemaker amongst your friends. People always ask you for advice because you are trustworthy and wise.

Mostly Cs: You are like Chopper. You can be a bit moody, but you are there when your friends need you. You provide comic relief to any stressful situation.

Mostly Ds: You are like Sabine. You are wild and creative, and can always be counted on to put together a scheme!

I'M A REBEL!!

You have proven yourself to be a rebel ally. Draw yourself in rebel gear here. Don't forget your weapons and add in your friends and a ship if you want to.

JUSTICE

JEDI
USE THE FORCE

REBELS ANSWERS

Page 9 REBELS READY:

Page 7 REBELLIOUS FRIENDS:

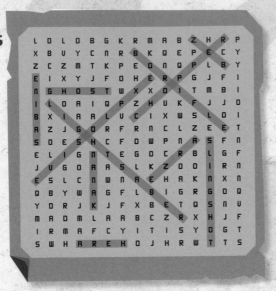

Page 11 KANAN'S CODE:

Jedi Order, The rise of the sith.

NOW FLIP OVER TO THE REBEL SIDE

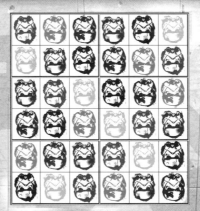

Page 32 STORMTROOPER SUDOKU:

Page 33-34 STICKER BOMB!

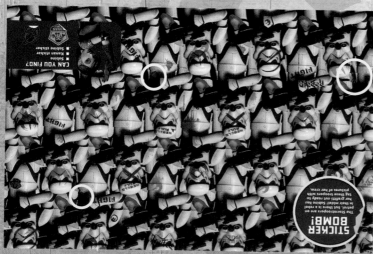

CAN YOU FIND?

☐ Sabine

☐ Kanan sticker

☐ Sabine sticker

The Stormtroopers are on patrol, but there is a rebel in their midst! Sabine has her graffiti out ready to tag these troopers with pictures of her crew.

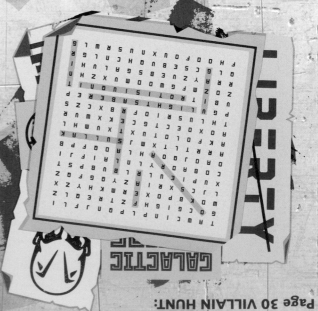

Page 30 VILLAIN HUNT:

Page 13
RACE TO THE COCKPIT:

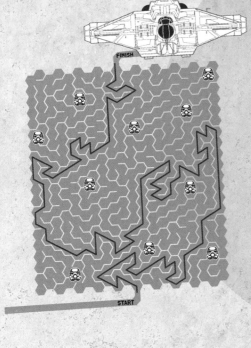

Page 23
DROID IN DISGUISE:

NOW FLIP OVER TO THE DARK SIDE

Page 33 STARSHIP SAILING:
Exit D is the right exit

START

A B C D

Page 21 WORD LADDERS

WHITE	SNOW
WHINE	SHOW
SHINE	SHOP
SPINE	SHIP
SPICE	SLIP
SLICE	SLID
SLICK	SAID
SLACK	RAID
BLACK	RAIN
	RAIL
	HAIL

Page 17 SUPPORT YOUR EMPIRE:

Page 13 WHO'S NEXT:

A: Inquisitor, Agent Kallus
B: Inquisitor, stormtrooper
C: Aresko, Grint
D: Stormtrooper, Agent Kallus

Page 9 MILITARY MAZE:

START

FINISH

Page 19 TIE TRIO:

EMPIRES ANSWERS

CAN YOU FIND?
- Sabine
- Kanan sticker
- Sabine sticker

35

STAR WARS REBELS™

ANNUAL 2015

First published in Great Britain 2014
by Egmont UK Limited, The Yellow Building,
1 Nicholas Road, London W11 4AN.

Designed by Maddox Philpot. Written by Katrina Pallant.

© 2014 Lucasfilm Ltd. & ™. All rights reserved.

ISBN 978 1 4052 7201 8
57508/1
Printed in Italy

Stay safe online. Any website addresses listed in this book are correct at the
time of going to print. However, Egmont is not responsible for content hosted by
third parties. Please be aware that online content can be subject to change
and websites can contain content that is unsuitable for children.
We advise that all children are supervised
when using the internet.

CONTENTS

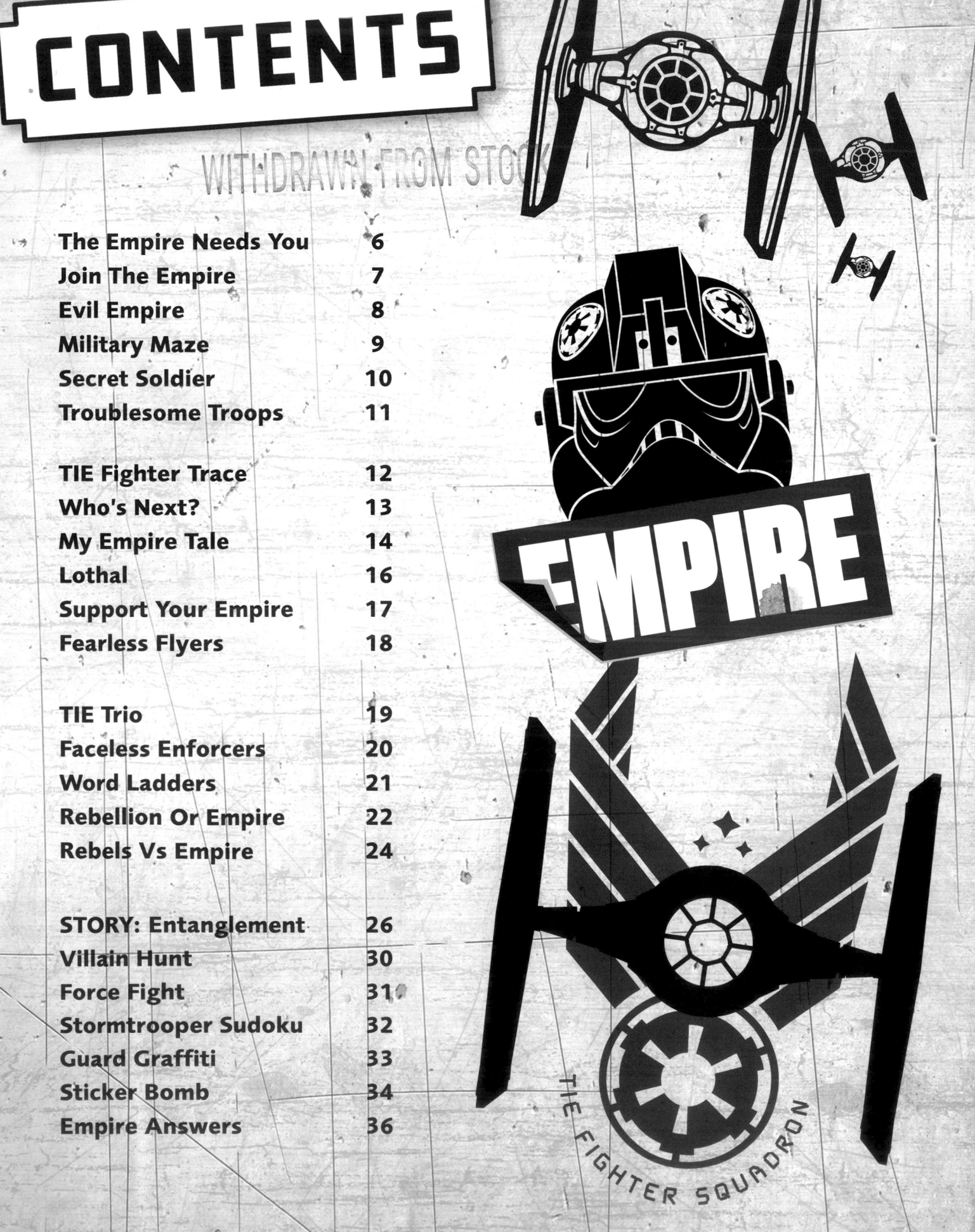

WITHDRAWN FROM STOCK

EMPIRE

THE FIGHTER SQUADRON

THE EMPIRE NEEDS YOU!

The Galactic Empire promises peace and security to a war-weary galaxy. The Clone Wars have left many worlds, especially Lothal, impoverished and without purpose. The Empire offer jobs in their TIE fighter factories and as officers in the Imperial Fleet for ambitious Lothalians. They have taken control of the weak government and are bringing order and safety to the citizens. Rebels threaten to destroy this with their terrorist acts and must be sought out and brought to justice.

WHAT ROLE WILL YOU PLAY IN THE EMPIRE?
WRITE YOUR STATS HERE.

Name: _____

World: _____

Species: _____

Job:　　　**Stormtrooper / Imperial officer / Commander / TIE fighter builder /**
Government official (circle your choice)

Favourite way to take down a rebel:

In battle / By having superior equipment / Through interrogation /
Bringing them to justice through the courts (circle your choice)

Favourite weapon:

Blaster / Explosive / Lightsaber / The Law (circle your choice)

Favourite mode of transport:

TIE fighter / Starfighter / On foot patrol (circle your choice)

JOIN THE EMPIRE

**Draw yourself as an Imperial Officer.
Don't forget to customise your uniform and weapon!**

7

EVIL EMPIRE

NAME: THE **INQUISITOR**

INQUISITOR

MISSION

To track down and interrogate Jedi survivors and citizens with Force-sensitivity or potential. A cold and menacing villain, the Inquisitor is a tricky opponent for the rebels.

Species:
Pau'an

Homeworld:
Utapau

Special skills:
Force-sensitive, incredible intelligence – can work out an opponent's capability before he even makes a move

Signature equipment:
Unique ring-hilted lightsaber that he can spin and throw in combat

8

MILITARY MAZE

FINISH

The Inquisitor can sense the Force is strong in Ezra. Help him through the maze so he can interrogate the potential Jedi. Avoid Ezra's rebel friends.

START

SECRET SOLDIER

NAME: AGENT **KALLUS**

IMPERIAL

MISSION

To monitor loyalty to the Empire on Lothal. Kallus is a member of the Imperial Security Bureau – the Empire's secret police force intent on striking down rebels. He is a smart and dangerous foe and strikes fear in the hearts of even the most seasoned Imperial officers.

Species:
Human

Homeworld:
Unknown

Special skills:
Highly-skilled pilot, excellent in hand-to-hand combat

Signature equipment:
Traditional Lasat weapon – taken during the destruction of Lasan

TROUBLESOME TROOPS

Aresko   Grint

Commandant Aresko and Taskmaster Grint are members of the Imperial fleet. They wear the Imperial uniform, carry out Imperial orders and defend Imperial values, but they do not have Imperial wit.

These two officers are based on Lothal, tasked with keeping people in line and stopping rebel activity, but these unlikely soldiers are constantly outwitted by the *Ghost* crew.

Vizago

Cikatro Vizago is a Devaronian without morals. He only cares about one thing: money. He is a regular at the black market, selling luxury goods that have become very hard to come by under the new Lothalian government. He pays well to have his cargo moved off planet, no questions asked. Vizago's loyalty lies only with himself, and he will support whichever side of the conflict ensures his own survival.

TIE FIGHTER TRACE

Draw and colour in your very own Imperial ship. Use the grid to help you copy the TIE fighter.

WHO'S NEXT?

Look at these sequences and write the name of (or draw if you are feeling creative) the villains who come next.

A.

B.

C.

D.

TIME TO HELP THE EMPIRE BY CREATING SOME PROPAGANDA FOR THEM. CREATE YOUR OWN RECRUITMENT POSTER ON THIS PAGE, AND THEN ON THE NEXT PAGE WRITE, DRAW AND COLOUR YOUR OWN IMPERIAL ADVENTURE.

THE INQUISITOR HAS LANDED ON LOTHAL TO SEEK OUT A FORMER JEDI. COLOUR IN THIS FORMIDABLE AGENT.

THE INQUISITOR BRINGS IN AGENT KALLUS TO HELP HIM TRACK DOWN THE FORCE-SENSITIVE REBEL. DRAW KALLUS HERE.

THE INQUISITOR HAS FOUND KANAN, A FORMER JEDI KNIGHT. WRITE AN EPIC BATTLE STORY OF THIS LIGHTSABER DUEL.

LOTHAL

Name: Lothal

Region:
Outer Rim Territories

Landscape:
Mountain ranges, grassland savannahs

Indigenous races:
None, inhabited by settlers from human, Rodian, Aqualish, Gotal and many other races

Employment:
Farming, factory work

Affiliation:
Galactic Empire

Economy:
Poor

Lothal's government collaborated with the Imperial occupation. Lothal is very valuable to the Empire so the prime locations around the factories are well-patrolled; it is not unusual to see TIE fighters in the sky and there is even a Star Destroyer on-hand for protection. Stormtroopers are always on the look-out for rebel activity.

Lothal has been under Imperial occupation for many years. The planet has a lot of rich, natural resources, which makes it an attractive prospect for the Empire, but its location in the outer rim also makes it a perfect navigational point for a new hyperspace path.

Lothal's primary industry is farming, but the Empire was not interested in foodstuffs, only in the minerals and metals under the surface that could be used for their war machines. Many small independent farms were seized from their owners, drilled into for raw materials and then built upon for vehicle and weapon factories.

SUPPORT YOUR EMPIRE

Propaganda posters are everywhere in Lothal, recruiting Lothalians to join the Imperial forces and build TIE fighters for the fleet. Can you spot five differences between these two posters?

LONG LIVE THE GALACTIC

EMPIRE

LONG LIVE THE GALACTIC

EMPIRE

Colour in a TIE fighter for every difference you find.

FEARLESS FLYERS

TIE fighter stands for
Twin Ion Engine Fighters.

TIE FIGHTER

TIE fighter pilots are the dominant warriors of the sky. These Starfleet pilots have been highly-trained at the Imperial academy.

TIE fighters are produced in the thousands as they are cheap to make and are a key Imperial symbol. They are designed to attack in large numbers. All TIE fighters are fitted with a pair of very powerful laser cannons.

These vessels are entirely dependent on carrier ships when travelling through space as they do not have hyperdrive systems.

On Lothal, TIE fighters are used to patrol the skies and seek out rebel activity.

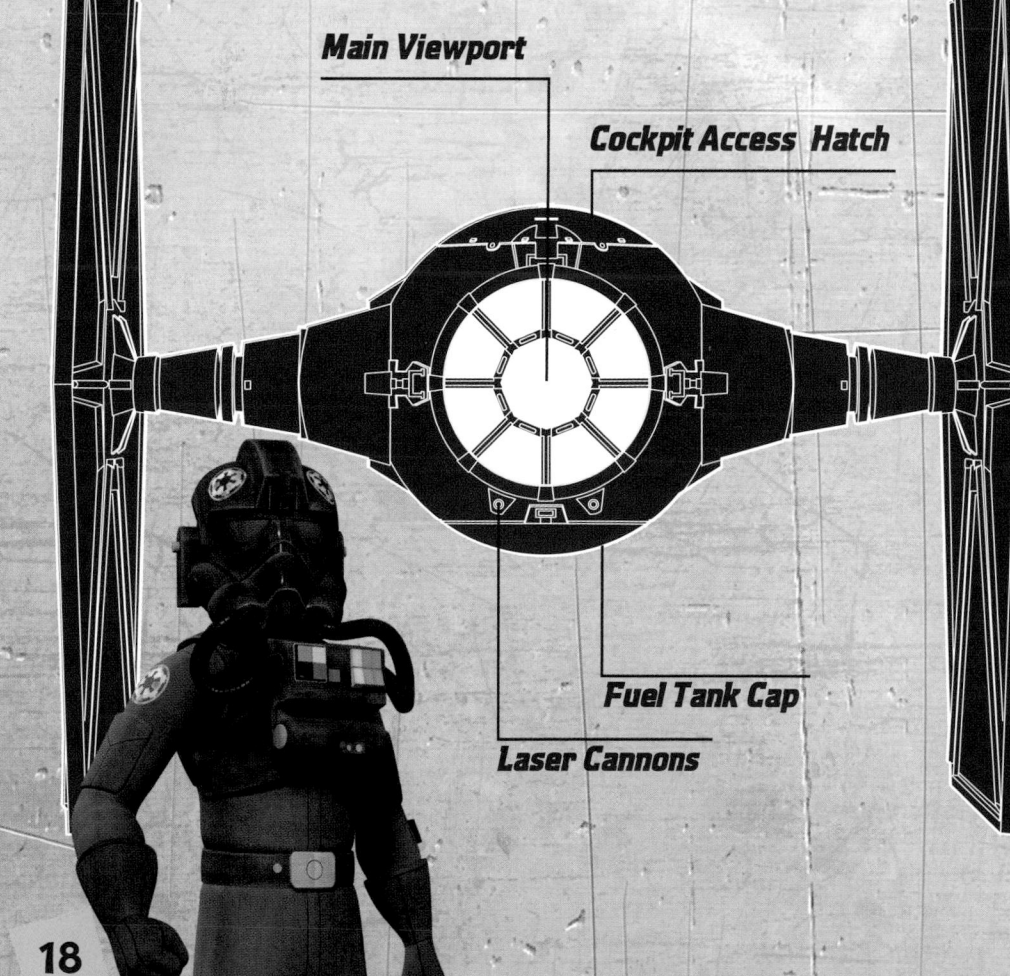

Main Viewport

Cockpit Access Hatch

Fuel Tank Cap

Laser Cannons

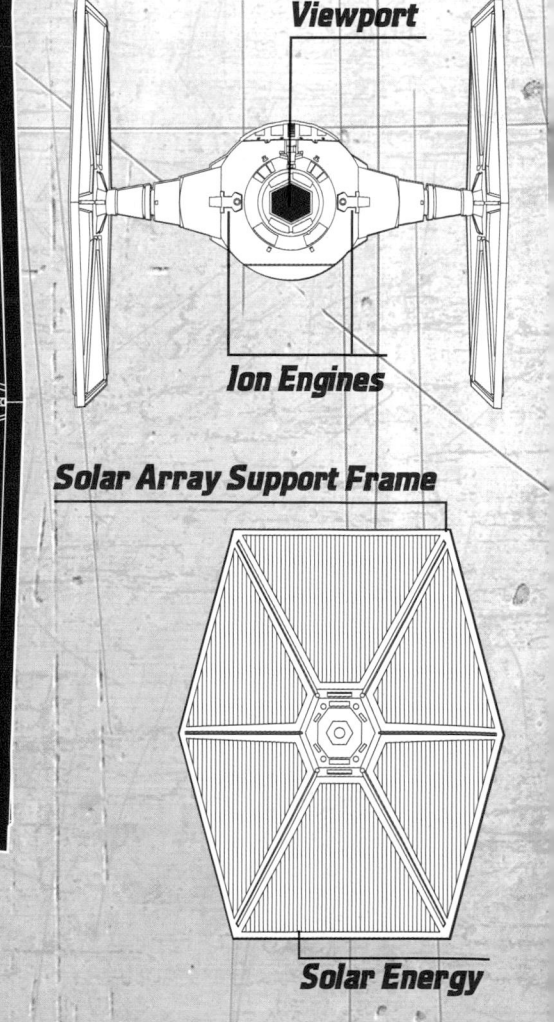

Viewport

Ion Engines

Solar Array Support Frame

Solar Energy

TIE TRIO

TIE fighters fight in groups. Can you match up these TIE fighters into identical threes so that they all have wingmen?

FACELESS ENFORCERS

STORM TROOPER

NICKNAMES:

STORMIES, WHITEHATS, BUCKETHEADS

Stormtroopers are traditionally highly-trained soldiers of the Galactic Empire – during the Clone Wars they were almost exclusively clones dedicated to carrying out the will of the Emperor with military precision and obedience. Now they are mostly men and women who have been recruited by the Empire and trained for duty. They are not always well-equipped for battle, and this allows the rebels to continually thwart them with clever tricks and schemes.

STORMTROOPER

WHITE ARMOUR IS EASILY RECOGNISED AND CONSIDERED IMPOSING TO THE ENEMY.

HELMET EQUIPPED WITH INTERNAL COMLINK AND AN EXTERNAL LIGHT.

ALL STORMTROOPERS CARRY A THERMAL DETONATOR THAT CAN ONLY BE ACTIVATED BY THEM.

BLASTER PISTOL IS THE STANDARD ISSUE WEAPON FOR STORMTROOPERS. POWERFUL AND COMPACT BUT NOT ALWAYS ACCURATE.

EQUIPPED WITH SURVIVAL EQUIPMENT AND TEMPERATURE CONTROLS SO STORMTROOPERS COULD OPERATE IN ANY ENVIRONMENT.

WORD LADDERS

Stormtroopers can survive in almost any weather in their high-tech suits. Can you get from snow to hail by only changing one letter at a time? There are clues to help you.

Stormtroopers wear white because it is intimidating to the enemy. Can you get from white to black by only changing one letter at a time? There are clues to help you.

SNOW

_____ DEMONSTRATE

_____ PLACE TO BUY THINGS

_____ LARGE BOAT

_____ LOSE YOUR BALANCE

SLID

_____ MOVED SMOOTHLY

_____ UTTERED, SPOKE

_____ ATTACK

_____ WET WEATHER

_____ POST OR POLE

HAIL

WHITE

_____ COMPLAIN, MOAN

_____ RADIATE, LIKE THE SUN

_____ BACKBONE

SPICE

_____ GINGER, PEPPER, FOR EXAMPLE

_____ PIECE OF BREAD

_____ OILY, GREASY

_____ LOOSE

BLACK

REBELLION OR EMPIRE

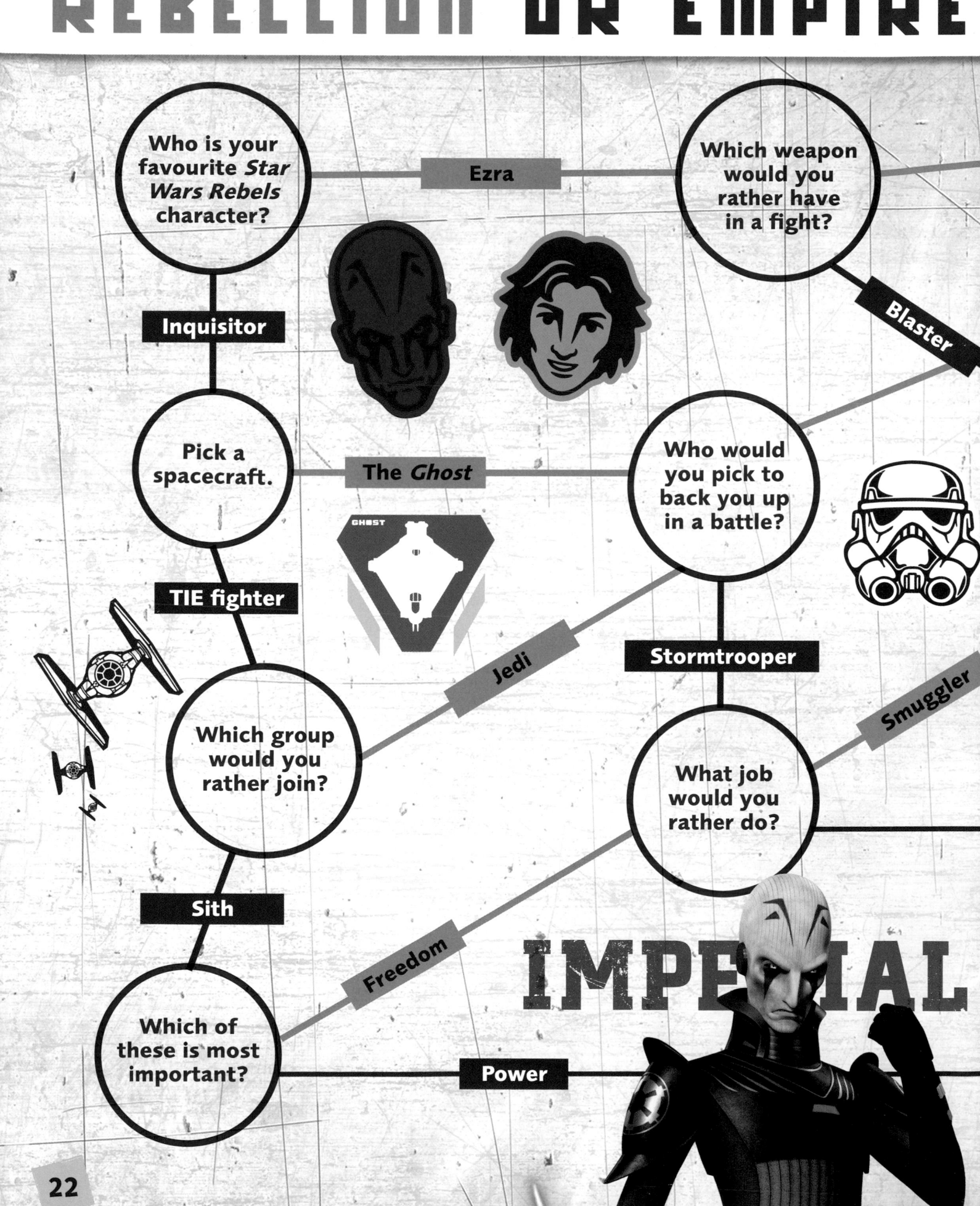

Who is your favourite *Star Wars Rebels* character?

Ezra

Which weapon would you rather have in a fight?

Inquisitor

Blaster

Pick a spacecraft.

The *Ghost*

GHOST

Who would you pick to back you up in a battle?

TIE fighter

Jedi

Stormtrooper

Smuggler

Which group would you rather join?

What job would you rather do?

Sith

Freedom

IMPERIAL

Which of these is most important?

Power

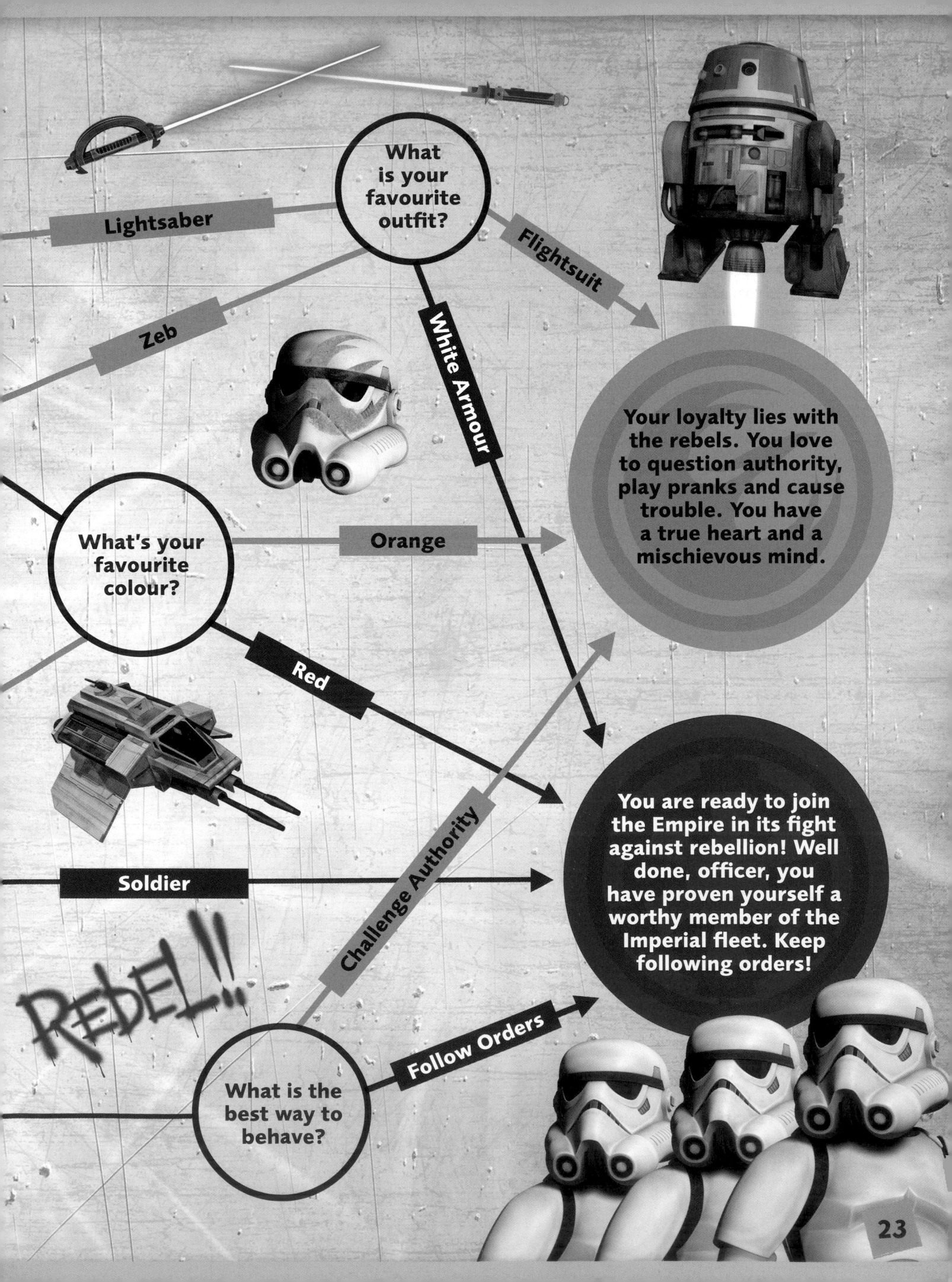

Lightsaber

What is your favourite outfit?

Flightsuit

Zeb

White Armour

What's your favourite colour?

Orange

Your loyalty lies with the rebels. You love to question authority, play pranks and cause trouble. You have a true heart and a mischievous mind.

Red

Soldier

Challenge Authority

You are ready to join the Empire in its fight against rebellion! Well done, officer, you have proven yourself a worthy member of the Imperial fleet. Keep following orders!

REBEL!!

Follow Orders

What is the best way to behave?

You and a friend must pick who is going to be a rebel and who is going to represent the Empire. Then play these awesome games!

THREE IN A ROW

Take it in turns to put either 'R' (for rebel) or 'E' (for Empire) in the grid. The first one to get three in a row is the winner!

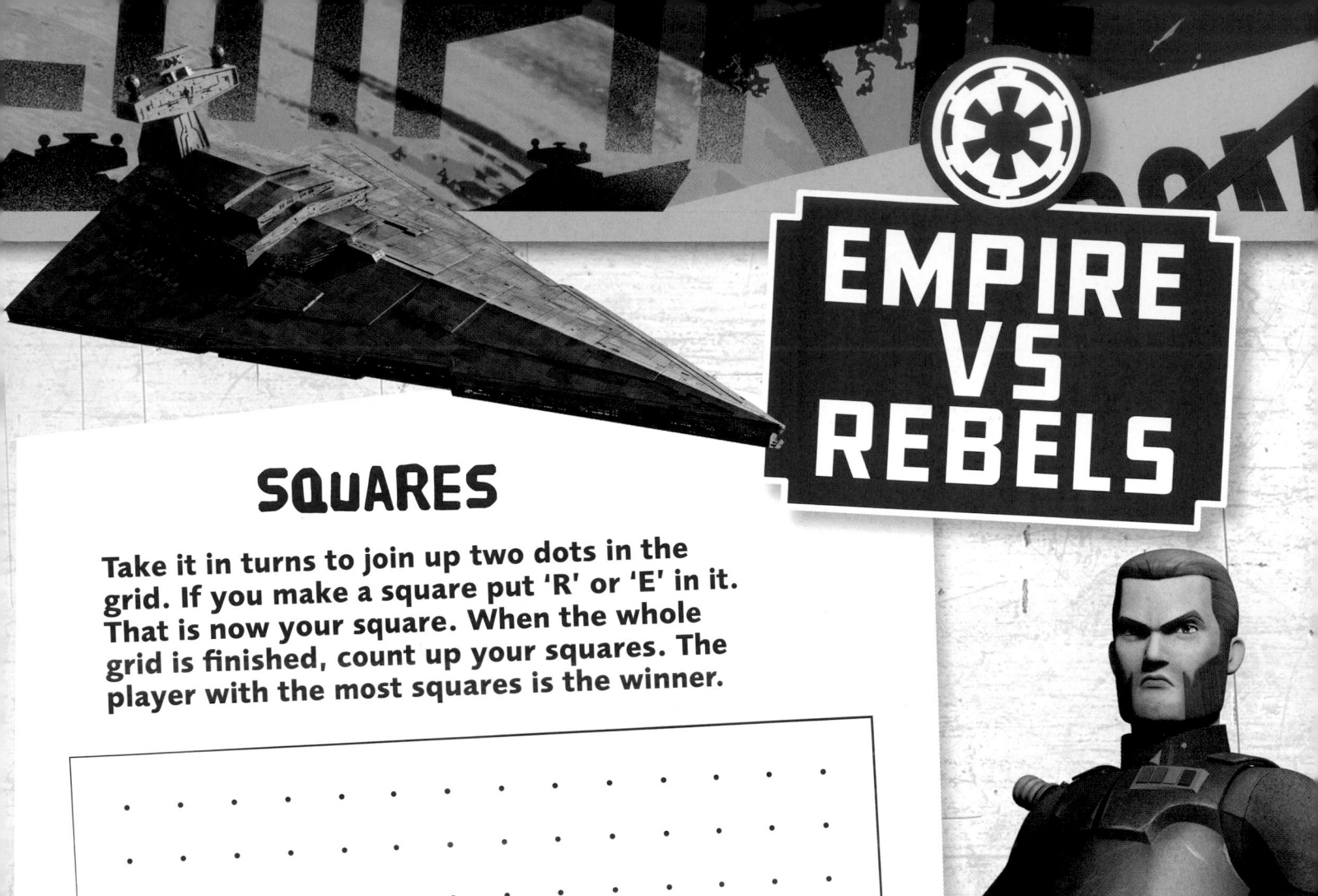

SQUARES

Take it in turns to join up two dots in the grid. If you make a square put 'R' or 'E' in it. That is now your square. When the whole grid is finished, count up your squares. The player with the most squares is the winner.

ENTANGLEMENT

Zeb is in an abandoned alley in Capital City. He looks around, confused.

'Zeb! Where are you?' asks Kanan, over the radio.
'I'm at the rendezvous point,' replies Zeb. 'Where are you?'
'You're not at the rendezvous point, because I'm at the rendezvous point,' Kanan says.

'Uh, where's the rendezvous point again?'
'In the alley by the marketplace.'
Zeb looks around but he can't see Kanan. He does however see two stormtroopers approach the marketplace.
'Well, I'm in an alley.'

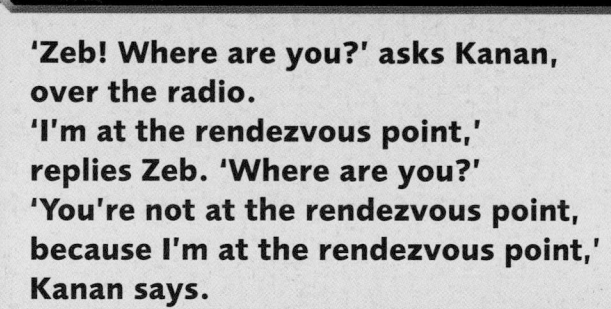

Zeb angrily observes the stormtroopers harassing a vendor selling fruit from a crate. As the stormtroopers kick over the vendor's droid, Zeb clenches his fists and prepares to fight.

The vendor is frightened by the imposing Imperial officers. He pleads with the stormtroopers, offering them some money to leave him alone..

'What? Is that a bribe?' one of the stormtroopers says. 'I can't believe it! That is an offence! Stop whining. We're here to protect you,' he continues as he clears out the vendor's credit box.

Suddenly, Zeb appears, slams the two troopers together hard and drops them to the ground. The vendor is very grateful.

'So are you going to make the rendezvous or not?' interjects Kanan. Zeb sees four more stormtroopers running up the alley towards him. 'It's possible I may be a little late.'

'Zeb, what's going on?' Kanan asks as Zeb runs to a nearby landing pad. A TIE fighter pilot is checking his ship when he notices the rebel. 'This is a restricted area!' he cries, before Zeb knocks him out with a single punch.

SMACK!

Zeb runs to the mouth of the alley and hides behind a wall when he sees four Troopers approaching. When the soldiers come near, Zeb grabs one and swings him into the others, knocking them down.

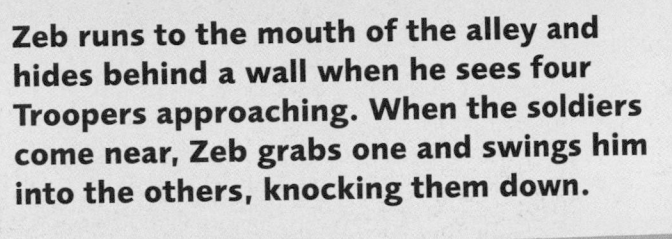

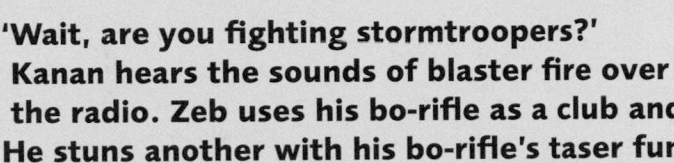

'Wait, are you fighting stormtroopers?' Kanan hears the sounds of blaster fire over the radio. Zeb uses his bo-rifle as a club and knocks a stormtrooper off his feet. He stuns another with his bo-rifle's taser function sending the trooper flying. 'Oh that's great,' says Kanan. 'You get lost in the middle of a mission and decide to start your own battle. Again!'

'Didn't decide. It just happened. This time,' replies Zeb, as the TIE fighter pilot calls for reinforcements. The commander asks the pilot how many intruders there are. Zeb pretends to count. 'One,' he shouts as he leaps up onto the TIE fighter and swings around to avoid the pilot's blaster fire.

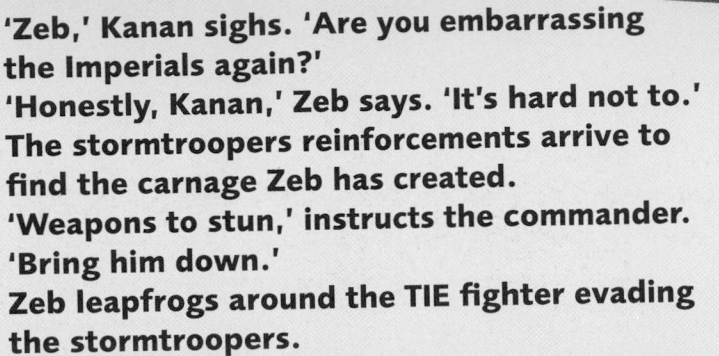

'Zeb,' Kanan sighs. 'Are you embarrassing the Imperials again?'

'Honestly, Kanan,' Zeb says. 'It's hard not to.' The stormtroopers reinforcements arrive to find the carnage Zeb has created.

'Weapons to stun,' instructs the commander. 'Bring him down.'

Zeb leapfrogs around the TIE fighter evading the stormtroopers.

'Can't get a clear shot!' shouts a stormtrooper. 'I mean do they even bother training these bucket-heads?' Zeb complains as he continues hopping about. 'My old gran's a better fighter, and she's only two metres tall!'

'Weapons on kill!' shouts the commander. The stormtroopers who are still standing fire their blasters at the TIE fighter. Zeb pokes his head under the fuselage to check on his opponents, but is shocked to see the TIE fighter is leaking fuel. 'Well, that's not good,' he says.'What's not good?' shouts Kanan, worrying what trouble his crewmate has gotten himself into. Zeb scrambles away as the TIE fighter explodes, launching stormtroopers in every direction.

The nervous vendor and droid approach the crash site just as Zeb saunters away. The vendor offers him his credit box, grateful for this hero's help. Zeb instead takes a single piece of fruit as thanks.
'Zeb! I see smoke,' Kanan says over the radio. 'Was that a TIE fighter exploding?'
'No,' Zeb lies. 'OK, yes.'
'Nice.' Kanan is impressed. 'OK, stay put. I'll follow the smoke and pick you up.' Zeb smiles and takes out his weapon as more stormtroopers run into the alley. 'I'll be right here.'

THE END.

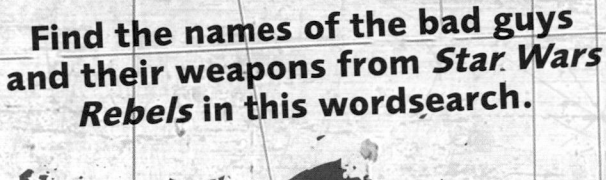

VILLAIN HUNT

Find the names of the bad guys and their weapons from *Star Wars Rebels* in this wordsearch.

```
T A W C I N P L P Q N J F L I
G O C G I G H F Z T R E Q F L Z
W D K B P O X E R M K H Y L X X
L J C S X P R I A Z Q G F Q Z T
X U P I E U L R L B U B P S I B
C D B A D R Y L N L A G I P A K
D A O J Q O A H L A D Q F J T I B
A R R T L X T M J S L G P A H K
K F O L O E T U X T X U M H U Z
A X D E C T G C E K X X W R Z R
T L U S R I D F R B X C Z S P R
P G U L I G H T S A B E R E E P
U B I T R O T I S I U Q N I T N
Z D Z Y F G W D D M U X Z H D I
R R A Y Z U E B S G A L V U R G
Q L G C S E B U Q H C N L G R L
F H O D F O U X N U S R W L G
```

| Inquisitor | Grint | Kallus | Fear |
| Vizago | Aresko | Blaster | Lightsaber |

30

FORCE FIGHT

DARK SIDE

JEDI

The Inquisitor and Kanan are mortal enemies. Colour in this fighting pair as they wield their lightsabers and channel the Force.

STORMTROOPER SUDOKU

The stormtroopers have had their helmets graffitied by the rebels. Fill in the gaps by writing the colour of the missing helmet. There must be one of each helmet in every row, column and box.

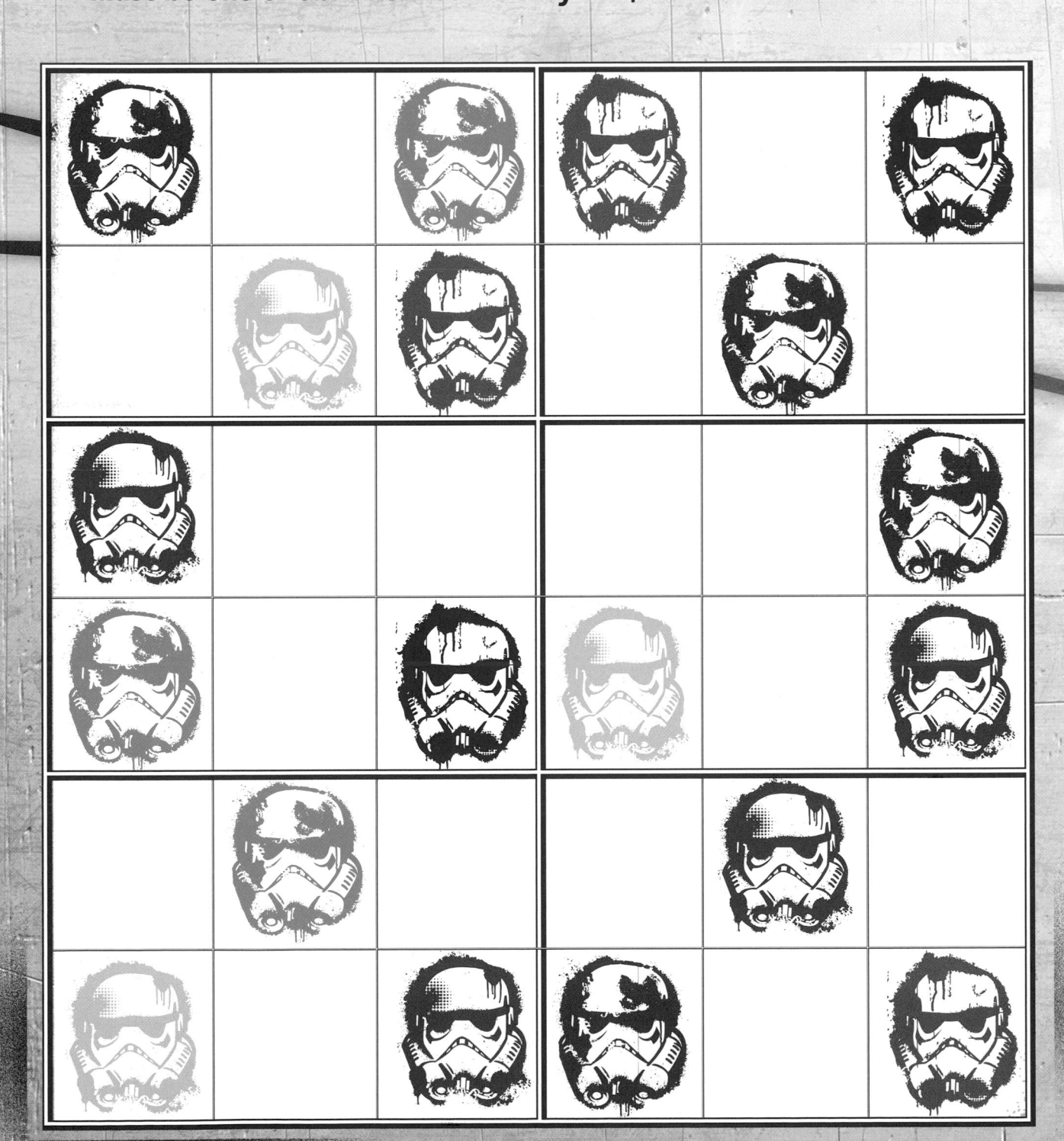

GUARD GRAFFITI

Stormtroopers' uniforms are always white –
brighten them up with some graffiti and colour!

STICKER BOMB!

The stormtroopers are on patrol, but there is a rebel in their midst! Sabine has her graffiti out ready to tag these troopers with pictures of her crew.

34